INDRA AND SHACHI

INDRA WAS THE KING OF THE DEVAS. HE LIVED WITH HIS QUEEN, SHACHI IN HIS CELESTIAL CITY, AMARAVATI.

LORD! WE ARE SO HAPPY THAT I FEAR IT MIGHT NOT LAST.

NOTHING UNTOWARD CAN HAPPEN TO US, MY DEAR.

BUT THERE WAS CAUSE FOR THEM TO FEAR. AT THAT VERY MOMENT A SON WAS BORN TO TVASHTA, INDRA'S ENEMY.

MY SON, YOU SHALL BECOME KING OF THE GODS.

YOU SHALL RECITE THE VEDAS WITH ONE HEAD...

...CONSUME THE DIVINE SURA WITH THE OTHER AND...

...WATCH THE WORLD WITH THE THIRD.

TRISHIRAS GREW UP FAST. HE BECAME STRONG-WILLED AND POWERFUL.

I SHALL PERFORM SEVERE PENANCES AND DESTROY INDRA, MY FATHER'S ENEMY.

INDRA HEARD OF TRISHIRAS AND OF HIS INTENSE PENANCE TO DESTROY HIM. HE SENT FOR THE APSARAS, THE CELESTIAL MAIDENS...

YOU MUST DISTRACT TRISHIRAS AND BREAK HIS PENANCE.

WE WILL LEAD HIM AWAY FROM MEDITATION INTO A LIFE OF PLEASURE.

THE APSARAS PREPARED THEMSELVES.

WE WILL TEMPT HIM WITH THESE FRUITS AND FLOWERS.

I WILL DANCE.

YOUR VOICE IS SWEET AND ENCHANT- ING. YOU MUST SING.

THEIR CHARMS WERE HEAVENLY. BUT TRISHIRAS WAS UNMOVED.

THE APSARAS RETURNED TO INDRA.

WE HAVE FAILED. TRISHIRAS IS STEADFAST...

AT THIS RATE HE WILL USURP MY THRONE. I MUST KILL HIM.

SHACHI WAS WORRIED.

BE CAREFUL! I FEAR FOR YOUR SAFETY.

INDRA THREW HIS THUNDERBOLT AT TRISHIRAS WHILE HE WAS PRAYING.

TRISHIRAS FELL DEAD BUT HIS EYES REMAINED UNSHUT AND STARING.

THOSE EYES HAUNT ME.

I MUST GET THEM CLOSED.

THEY DRAIN ME OF ALL MY STRENGTH.

AT THAT MOMENT A WOODCUTTER HAPPENED TO PASS BY.

PLEASE CUT HIS HEADS OFF WITH YOUR AXE.

HIS NECK IS TOO THICK. MY AXE WILL BECOME BLUNT.

MY THUNDER-BOLT SHALL GIVE IT AN EDGE, FINE AND STRONG.

THE WOODCUTTER CUT TRISHIRAS' HEADS OFF.

5

NOW I WILL HAVE TO ATONE FOR MY SIN. I HAVE MURDERED A BRAHMAN.

INDRA DID PENANCE FOR A LONG TIME.

FINALLY, A DIVINE VOICE SPOKE TO HIM.

ARISE, INDRA. YOU HAVE ATONED FOR YOUR SIN BY YOUR PENANCE.

NOW I AM FREE. I SHALL RETURN TO AMARAVATI.

I HAVE COME HOME VICTORIOUS.

THANKS BE TO GOD.

6

MEANWHILE TVASHTA HEARD OF TRISHIRAS' DEATH. HE WAS DEEPLY GRIEVED AND VERY ANGRY.

I SHALL AVENGE MY SON'S DEATH. FROM THE POWER OF MY PRAYERS...

...SHALL RISE AN ASURA.

TVASHTA PERFORMED A SACRIFICE AND CREATED AN ASURA.

YOU ARE VRITRA. GO FORTH AND KILL INDRA.

WHEN INDRA HEARD OF VRITRA, HE PREPARED TO MEET THE CHALLENGE.

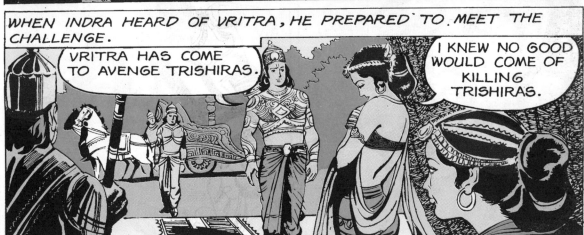

VRITRA HAS COME TO AVENGE TRISHIRAS.

I KNEW NO GOOD WOULD COME OF KILLING TRISHIRAS.

THERE WAS A TERRIBLE BATTLE IN WHICH VRITRA CAUGHT INDRA BETWEEN HIS TEETH.

HE HAS CAUGHT INDRA.

QUICK! HAND ME THE *JRIMBHAKA ASTRA.

THE JRIMBHAKA ASTRA FOUND ITS MARK.

I CANNOT CONTROL THESE YAWNS. THAT ASTRA DOES IT.

THIS IS THE MOMENT FOR ME.

VRITRA YAWNED...

INDRA MADE HIMSELF TINY AND ESCAPED.

* AN ARROW WHICH MAKES A MAN YAWN.

8

HE AND HIS SUBJECTS WENT TO VISHNU FOR ADVICE.

LORD, HELP US.

MAKE PEACE WITH VRITRA. THEN WATCH FOR YOUR CHANCE TO KILL HIM. I WILL HELP YOU.

INDRA MADE PEACE WITH VRITRA. BUT VRITRA WAS WARY.

LET US BE FRIENDS! I ADMIRE YOU!

ALL RIGHT. BUT ON MY CONDITIONS.

YOU MUST NOT KILL ME WITH ANY WEAPON- WET OR DRY, OF WOOD OR OF STONE...

...BY DAY OR BY NIGHT!

I AGREE.

ONE EVENING THEY WERE ON THE SEA-SHORE.

I MUST KILL HIM SOON -BUT WITHOUT USING A WEAPON.

FOAM CANNOT BE CONSIDERED A WEAPON. VISHNU HAS PROMISED TO HELP ME.

THIS TWILIGHT IS NEITHER NIGHT NOR DAY. FOAM IS NEITHER WET NOR DRY. VISHNU, HELP ME!

VISHNU ENTERED THE FOAM AND WHEN INDRA THREW IT AT VRITRA, HE WAS KILLED IMMEDIATELY BY THE POWER OF VISHNU WITHIN IT.

BUT AS INDRA HAD BETRAYED VRITRA HE WAS ASHAMED TO FACE THE WORLD.

I HAVE KILLED VRITRA. BUT I CANNOT SHOW MY FACE TO ANYONE.

I SHALL HIDE WHERE NONE CAN FIND ME.

INDRA RAN AWAY. ALL WAS DARKNESS AND CHAOS, ON EARTH AND IN HEAVEN.

THERE IS NO LIGHT ANYWHERE.

OH! SOMEONE IS BEATING ME IN THE DARK.

HOW DARE YOU ENTER MY HOUSE?

THE DEVAS MET IN A COUNCIL.

WITHOUT A KING THE HEAVENS ARE IN CHAOS.

WE CANNOT ALLOW THIS ANARCHY TO GO ON.

INDRA HAS DESERTED US.

WE MUST FIND ANOTHER KING.

KING NAHUSHA IS A GOOD AND PIOUS MAN. SHALL WE SELECT HIM?

YES! YES!

LET US GO TO EARTH AND INVITE HIM TO BE OUR KING.

THE DEVAS WENT TO KING NAHUSHA'S COURT.

THE DEVAS MADE NAHUSHA THEIR KING.

BUT ALAS! NAHUSHA SOON BECAME CONCEITED AND ARROGANT.

WHO IS THAT BEING WHO GOES PAST WITHOUT BOWING TO HIS KING? BRING HIM HERE!

HEY, YOU SAGE THERE! COMPOSE A VERSE IN PRAISE OF ME.

IT IS HOT! LET ONE OF THE *MARUTS BLOW COOL BREEZE ON ME.

THE DEVAS WERE VERY UNHAPPY.

HE ORDERS US ABOUT AS IF WE WERE HIS SLAVES!

HE IS UNBEARABLE.

BE CAREFUL! HE MAY HEAR US!

* THE GODS OF WIND.

15

ONE DAY NAHUSHA SAW SHACHI IN THE PARK.

WHO IS THAT!

OUR QUEEN, SHACHI DEVI.

AS I AM THE KING HERE, SHE IS MY QUEEN.

GO AT ONCE AND BRING HER HERE!

DON'T DO THAT! SHE IS DEVOTED TO INDRA.

TERRIFIED, SHACHI RAN TO THE HOUSE OF BRIHASPATI, THE GURU OF THE DEVAS.

REVERED ONE, YOU KNOW I AM INDRA'S DEVOTED WIFE. SAVE ME FROM NAHUSHA.

DO NOT WORRY. YOU ARE SAFE HERE.

16

NAHUSHA WAS VERY ANGRY WHEN HE HEARD THAT SHACHI WAS IN BRIHASPATI'S HOUSE.

THE DEVAS TREMBLED BEFORE NAHUSHA'S FURY. THEY RAN TO BRIHASPATI'S HOUSE.

SHACHI CAME OUT AND MET THEM.

SO, PROMPTED BY BRIHASPATI, SHACHI WENT WITH THE DEVAS TO NAHUSHA.

FIRST LET US SEARCH FOR MY LORD. IF HE CANNOT BE FOUND I SHALL BECOME YOUR QUEEN.

THAT IS REASONABLE. I AGREE.

THE DEVAS THEN WENT TO VISHNU FOR ADVICE.

WE MUST RESCUE OUR QUEEN. TELL US WHAT WE SHOULD DO NOW!

FIND OUT INDRA AND MAKE HIM PERFORM AN ASHWAMEDHA TO ATONE FOR THE SIN OF KILLING VRITRA, BY DECEIT.

AGNI, THE FIRE-GOD, LED THE SEARCH FOR INDRA.

COME ON! WE WILL FIND HIM SOMEHOW.

YES, HE MUST BE FOUND.

AT LAST THEY FOUND INDRA.

YOU MUST PERFORM THE ASHWAMEDHA TO ATONE FOR YOUR SIN.

THEN YOU MUST COME AND ATTACK NAHUSHA.

INDRA PERFORMED THE ASHWAMEDHA...

...AND THEN SET OUT TO CHALLENGE NAHUSHA.

I DO NOT FEEL DESOLATE ANY MORE.

COME AND DRIVE OUT NAHUSHA.

SHACHI HEARD THAT INDRA WAS COMING.

MAY HE DEFEAT NAHUSHA.

SO DID NAHUSHA.

I MUST GET. INDRA OUT OF MY WAY.

INDRA CONFRONTED NAHUSHA.

HE IS TOO POWERFUL. I CANNOT FACE HIM.

THIS WEAKLING? IS THIS THE MIGHTY INDRA?

INDRA RAN AWAY.

WHY DO I QUAKE IN FEAR?

SHACHI WEPT.

I WOULD GIVE MY LIFE TO HELP HIM.

21

SHACHI PRAYED TO UPASHRUTI, A GODDESS OF THE NIGHT.

OH MIGHTY GODDESS! HELP ME!

UPASHRUTI APPEARED BEFORE SHACHI.

WHAT CAN I DO FOR YOU, MY CHILD?

MOTHER! TAKE ME TO MY LORD.

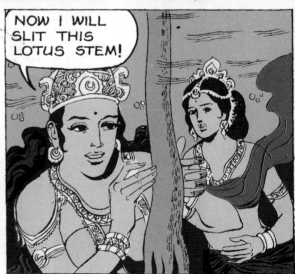

24

UPASHRUTI SLIT THE STEM. INSIDE COWERED A TINY INDRA.

HOW CAN I GET IN THERE AND SPEAK TO HIM?

I WILL MAKE YOU TINY LIKE HIM.

WHY DID YOU COME HERE?

LORD! YOU DO NOT KNOW MY PLIGHT.

AFTER SHACHI HAD EXPLAINED THE WHOLE SITUATION —

YOU MUST SAVE ME, OR NAHUSHA WILL MAKE ME HIS QUEEN TOMORROW.

INDRA TOLD HER WHAT SHE SHOULD DO.

GO QUICKLY AND DO AS I HAVE TOLD YOU.

I HOPE WE SUCCEED.

I HAVE FINISHED. LET US GO BACK.

THE NEXT MORNING SHACHI WENT TO NAHUSHA.

INDRA HAS RUN AWAY. I AM READY TO BE YOUR QUEEN.

I EXPECTED THIS.

INDRA USED TO COME TO MY PALACE...

"...SOMETIMES ON HIS WHITE ELEPHANT..."

"...SOMETIMES ON A HORSE..."

"...SOMETIMES IN HIS CHARIOT."

I HAVE A SPECIAL REQUEST TO MAKE. YOU SHOULD COME TO ME IN A PALANQUIN BORNE BY THE SEVEN SAGES.

THAT IS EASY. I AM THEIR KING. I WILL COME THIS EVENING.

TELL THE SEVEN SAGES TO BE READY TO CARRY MY PALANQUIN.

I SHALL PUT ON MY FINEST CLOTHES AND JEWELS.

NAHUSHA SET OUT IN THE PALANQUIN BORNE BY THE SEVEN SAGES.

28

MEANWHILE SHACHI WENT TO BRIHASPATI'S HOUSE.

I HAVE DONE MY PART.

THEN I SHALL SEND FOR INDRA.

BRIHASPATI INVOKED AGNI IN A SACRIFICE.

AGNI! YOU MUST FIND INDRA AND BRING HIM HERE, AT ONCE.

I WILL DO MY BEST. THE MARUTS WILL HELP ME MOVE QUICKLY.

AGNI CALLED THE DEVAS.

THE TIME HAS COME TO FORCE INDRA TO COME HERE.

WE WILL FOLLOW AS QUICKLY AS WE CAN.

WE WILL BLOW YOU AHEAD. THE OTHERS CAN FOLLOW.

AT THAT MOMENT NAHUSHA WAS ON HIS WAY TO SHACHI'S PALACE.

LAZY FELLOWS! HOW SLOW THEY ARE!

IT IS ALL THE FAULT OF AGASTYA. BECAUSE HE IS SHORT HE CANNOT KEEP PACE WITH THE OTHERS.

I SHALL GOAD HIM ON.

SARPA! SARPA!*

WHEN NAHUSHA KICKED HIM, AGASTYA BECAME ANGRY.

HOW DARE YOU! SARPO BHAVA** MY CURSE WILL TURN YOU INTO A SNAKE.

* MOVE ON. ALSO SNAKE.   30   ** MAY YOU BECOME A SNAKE.

BY THIS TIME THE DEVAS HAD FOUND INDRA.

BRIHASPATI ASKS YOU TO COME AT ONCE.

RETURN WITH US TO AMARAVATI.

WE WILL HELP YOU OUST NAHUSHA.

JUST THEN AGASTYA CAME HURRYING UP.

NAHUSHA IS NOW A MERE SNAKE.

WE ARE FREE AT LAST.

YOU ARE OUR KING ONCE MORE.

ONLY BECAUSE OF SHACHI'S LOYALTY TO ME!